DESMOND'S POSTBAG

edited and illustrated by Althea

ISBN 0-905-114-78-7 (paperback)
ISBN 0-905-114-84-1 (hardback)

Published by Bridge Street Books
LDA Duke Street Wisbech Cambridgeshire PE13 2AE

Stories

Desmond's First Friend

Desmond could not find a perfect friend,
not even Ichthyosaurus was good enough.
But when the dinosaurs ate all the eggs
he found that every dinosaur died
apart from him.
Then all the people came to earth and
he found they were better friends.

Desmond at the Circus

Desmond was very excited because
he was going to the circus.
He bought his seat in the back row.
The clowns made Desmond laugh and laugh.
One of the clowns threw an apple pie at the other.

At the interval Desmond had an ice-cream
and some delicious popcorn.

The next act was the trapeze.
Disaster happened.
High up, the trapeze artist
got the ropes tangled.
Desmond went quickly into the ring.
He put up his long neck
and the trapeze artist
slid down to safety.

Everyone clapped and cheered.
The ringmaster gave
Desmond a medal.

Desmond Hides under my Bed

One day I saw Desmond under my bed.
I asked him if he liked me.
He said, yes, and I will stay with you
until you are better.
I asked him what he was going to have
to eat and drink.
He said, fruit and vegetables are nice,
and you ought to eat some too.

I asked my mummy for an apple, a banana,
two lettuce leaves and a tomato.
Mummy did not know Desmond was going
to eat them, and was very pleased
I wanted them.

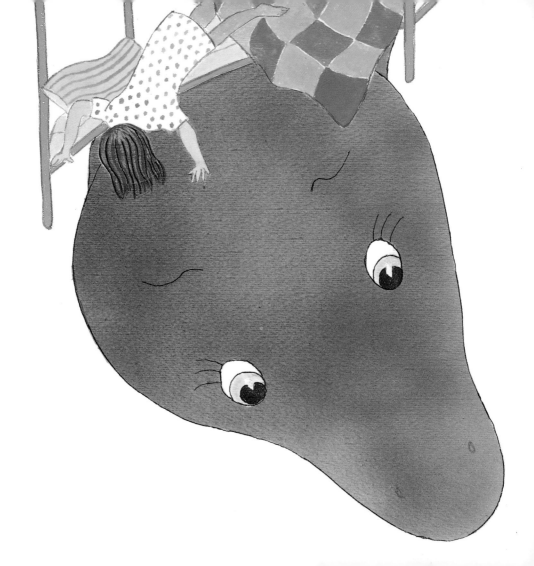

When Mummy brought them Desmond said
he would only eat some if I did.
I didn't want Desmond to get too thin,
so I ate some.
I soon got better and Desmond went back
with his Dinosaur family.

I am glad he hid under my bed to help me
get better, but he was growing so big
I could not hide him anymore.
I didn't want anybody to know my secret
of where all the fruit went.

Desmond the Gardener

Desmond was a dinosaur living after
his real time. His only friend was Mr Bell.
Desmond was having some oranges for
breakfast when he heard a shout.
It was Mr Bell, there was ivy all round
his tree.

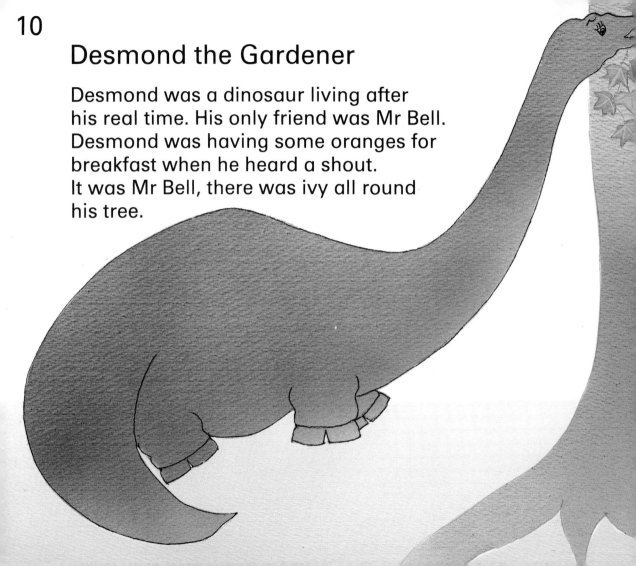

Mr Bell knew that Desmond ate plants,
so Mr Bell asked Desmond if he would eat
the ivy, so it wouldn't kill the tree.

Desmond started to eat the ivy.
When he had eaten it, he ate every weed
in the garden.
When he had finished, Mr Bell said,
'Thank you, how can I ever repay you?'
Desmond said, 'It was nothing,
I enjoyed doing it.'

Desmond gets a Parcel

Desmond was in bed.
His mum came up and said, 'You look ill.'
'I feel ill,' said Desmond.
One of Desmond's friends came round.
'Is Desmond coming out to play?'
'No,' said his Mum. 'He is ill.'

Then there was a knock at the door.
It was the postman, he handed Desmond's mum
a parcel. She gave it to Desmond,
because his name was on it.
Desmond opened it. It was a blue jersey.
He put on the jersey and went out to play.

'Parcels can bring some kids to life,'
said his mum.

Desmond Plays with the Children

Desmond liked going to the park
to see the children playing on
the swings and the slides.
But he felt very sad, because
every time he went to join in
the children ran away.
He didn't understand why,
because he liked their happy faces.

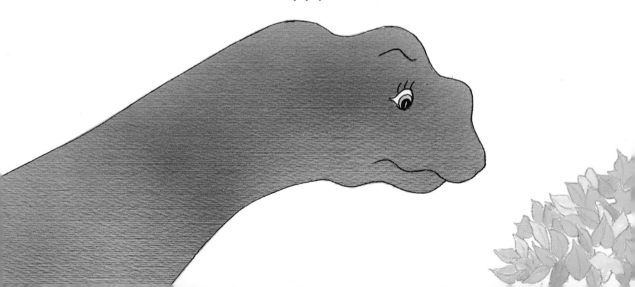

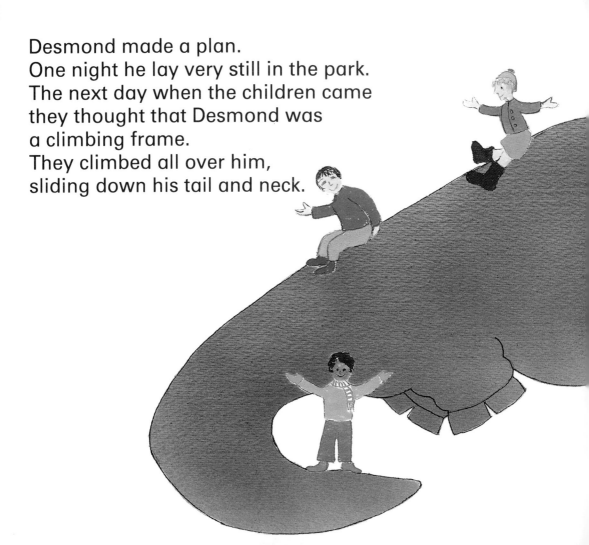

Desmond made a plan.
One night he lay very still in the park.
The next day when the children came
they thought that Desmond was
a climbing frame.
They climbed all over him,
sliding down his tail and neck.

When they found they had been climbing
on his back and having fun
they didn't run away.
Now Desmond sleeps in the park and
he is there when the children come
to play with him.

Desmond Fights the Monsters

Desmond was walking in the woods
when he saw some monsters who were fighting.
There was a Triceratops, a Tyrannosaurus Rex
and a Stegosaurus.
They were fierce and as big as houses.

Desmond said: 'STOP . . . it is too dangerous
to fight.'
They were wrecking the trees.
'Stop breaking the trees,' said Desmond.
They carried on fighting and
crushing the flowers.
'STOP STOP stop,' said Desmond again.
The dinosaurs were eating the fruit
from the trees.

Desmond broke up the fight.
He nearly got killed.
He was bruised and cut,
he had a black eye.

'We were fighting to get food,'
said the dinosaurs.
'We need food.'
'Then you must plant seeds and GROW food',
said Desmond.

Indian Music

Leela Floyd

Oxford University Press
Music Department
Walton Street, Oxford OX2 6DP

Contents

(Opposite) A market scene in Delhi, the capital of India ▶

India and its culture

What kind of place is India?

India is a very large country. You would have to walk every day for nearly a year to get from one end to the other. In the northernmost part are the snow-capped Himalayan mountains. The highest mountain in the world, Everest, is in the Himalayas. The southernmost tip is hot and full of coconut palms and sandy beaches. In Central India, there are jungles and barren deserts.

The people of India vary from north to south in their customs, language, religion, and looks. The people from the far north look like Europeans. People from the south are generally darker, because it is much hotter there and also because they are descendants of an ancient dark-skinned race.

There are many religions in India. But the religion that is followed by most people is **Hinduism**. It is one of the oldest religions in the world and the **Hindus** still worship in the same way as they did centuries ago.

The next most important religion is **Islam** which was brought to India by the Arabs in the 11th century. Other religions that Indians follow are Christianity, Jainism, Buddhism and Sikhism.

▲ Himalayan scene with Mount Everest in the background

◀ A sandy beach in the province of Orissa, Central India

India's history

One of the oldest civilizations in the world existed in India, near the river Indus, around 3000 B.C. At that time the Indians there were a highly civilized people who traded with the ancient Sumerians and Egyptians. Later the religion, arts, and Indian way of life fascinated people from other parts of the world. The Chinese and Greeks visited India and wrote books about the country and its people.

Since the earliest civilization, over 4000 years ago, India has been through many changes. About 2000 years ago the country was ruled by Hindu and Buddhist princes, some of whom lived rich and luxurious lives. The Hindu and Buddhist religions at this time spread to other countries — Indonesia, Thailand, Cambodia, Burma, China and Tibet.

A god towers above these young women in Nasik, near Bombay ▶

▼ A Jain temple in Bhubaneswar, Orissa, Central India

In the 11th century, India was invaded by Muslims who came from Turkey and Afghanistan. Many Hindus were forcibly converted to the Muslim religion — Islam (also the religion of the Arabs). Later on, during the 14th and 15th centuries, India was ruled by Muslim emperors called **Moghuls**. They introduced a new kind of music, art, religion and architecture into India. The Taj Mahal, for example, was built by a Moghul. The wealth of India attracted many other nations.

During the 17th century, the French, Portuguese and the British entered India. The British remained as the rulers of India until the 1940s. India then became independent, and split into Pakistan and India.

Indian people have also travelled and settled in other parts of the world. There are Indian communities in South America, North America, East and West Indies, Africa and Britain. They usually follow their own religion and way of life, but they also respect and try to understand the customs of people whose countries they have settled in.

▼ The most famous of all Indian monuments, the Taj Mahal, built by a Moghul emperor in memory of his wife. They are both buried there

Music, art and dance

The word for music in India is **sangita**. As well as music, its meaning includes dancing and drama. Dancing, singing, and playing an instrument were considered one single art. All the arts — poetry, art, drama, dance, and music — were thought to be a means of bringing people closer to God.

A series of paintings called **Ragamala** describes the mood of some of the tunes in Indian music. These specially composed tunes or scales called **ragas** are meant to create a particular mood or emotion. The artists of the Ragamala paintings created a picture of what they felt when they heard these ragas. For example, the painting of Raga Dipaka or 'Song of the earthen lamp' shows a prince seated on an elephant holding a flaming lamp on the tip of his trunk. The whole picture is meant to express the characteristic of the raga. You can see it on page 45. It is meant to convey an atmosphere of passion and heat.

▼ A Garba dance from Gujarat, north-west India. In this photo, the dancers are keeping time with tiny cymbals in both hands. (See page 13)

Many sculptures in temples show Gods and Goddesses playing musical instruments. There is one with the god Krishna playing the flute.

Music and dance were also closely connected with religion. There is one temple which has sculptures of different dance poses hewn out of stone.

Just as Western musicians and artists like Bach and Michelangelo were inspired by their love of God, so were the artists, craftsmen and musicians of India.

Questions

1   What is the meaning of the word *sangita*?
2   What do the Ragamala paintings describe?
3   How did musicians and sculptors combine their talents?
4   Which other arts combined with music?
5   Name a Western artist and a composer who were inspired by religion.

Projects

1   Make a drawing of an Indian temple, or any piece of Indian sculpture which shows a God or a Goddess with a musical instrument. You could copy one of the pictures from this book.
2   Trace the outline of the map on p. 47. On it mark the following: Himalayan mountains; Indian Ocean; the names of 3 states in the North; the names of 3 states in the South; the River Ganges; Calcutta; Delhi; Bombay; Madras.
3   Read the story of Raga Dipaka ('Song of the Earthen Lamp') in Chapter 5. Tell it in your own words.

Musicians and sculptors also got together and built unusual temples for the worship of God. For example, there is one temple in South India which has musical pillars. Each pillar plays a different note when struck softly. It is believed that these pillars were specially built to accompany the playing of musicians in the temple. Another temple has musical steps which sound notes when struck.

2 Five kinds of music

There are three main ways in which Indian people hear music: at the cinema, on the radio and at concerts. You have a choice of five different kinds of music: popular, folk, religious, classical, and western (that is, music from Europe and America).

Popular music

A favourite Indian pastime is going to the cinema. Most Indian films are musicals. So it is not surprising that the songs and music from films are more popular than any other type of music. India has the second largest film industry in the world (the largest is Hong Kong) and Indian films are shown all over the world. Most of the music that is played on All India Radio (the national radio of India) is popular film music.

Indian pop music has a huge market. You can buy records or cassettes of popular Indian music in countries like Morocco, Iran, Pakistan, other Eastern countries, Britain and the U.S.A. Nearly all Indian films are spoken in Hindi, the national language of India. This is why Indian pop music is usually called Hindi film music.

The music from the films is a blend of western and eastern musical styles. The bands that back up the songs use a selection of European and Indian instruments. For example, you can hear saxophones, violins, trumpets, pianos, bass guitars, and drums together with sitar, tabla and other Indian instruments.

Some well known songs from the British hit parade have been adapted and re-arranged to suit the Indian public. One example of a western pop tune used in this way is *The Young Ones* by Cliff Richard. The lyrics of the songs are very important, because they have been specially written to fit the story of the musical. One of the most popular Indian films at the moment is *Des*

◀ Scene from the film *Mother India*

(Title page) The famous Radha-Krishna dance which Indian children often learn. The goddess Radha was the wife of the god Krishna

▲ Scene from the film *Charulata* by India's most famous living film director, Satyajit Ray

Perdes which is based on a story about Indian immigrants living abroad. It is this musical which has an adaptation of the song *The Young Ones*.

Earlier films which were made in the 1940s and 1950s are still popular, and two outstanding ones are *Mother India* and *Janak Janak Payal Bhaji*. The names of some famous Indian actors and actresses are: Dev Anand, Raj Kapoor and Tina. Some important singers are Lata Mangeshkar, Kishore Kumar and Mohammed Rafi. Even though most Indian movies are musicals, there are some Indian directors who have made films that are not musicals. Films such as *The World of Apu* and *Charulata* were made as straight movies, and are popular with Western audiences.

Questions

1 What are the different kinds of music that you can hear in India?
2 What is unusual about Indian films?
3 What kind of music do the bands play in Indian musicals?
4 What is special about the lyrics in an Indian pop song?
5 What is unusual about the Indian film *Des Perdes*?

Project

Here is the tune of *The Young Ones* written in a slightly different way from the original tune. The chords can be played on a guitar, organ, harmonium or piano, and the rhythm on instruments like small cymbals, sticks, wood blocks, bongos, etc. The melody can be played on xylophones, glockenspiels, recorders or any other melodic instrument. The idea is to combine the sounds of western and Indian instruments, so that the song becomes more like an Indian pop tune. If anyone in the class can play an Indian instrument they can use it to play the tune or the rhythm.

11

Folk music

Folk music all over the world is about the feelings of ordinary people. The songs and tunes are made up and handed down from generation to generation without being written down.

The folk tradition in India began mainly because Indian people were not allowed to take part in religious music (which was the only type of music which existed at one time). Only the priests were allowed to perform sacred or religious music. So the ordinary village people made up their own kind of music which became known as **village music** or Indian folk music.

The folk songs have a special meaning or message. For example, the theme of a song may be a historical subject (like a battle or flood), a legend (story about a God or Goddess), or a subject from life (such as marriage, birth, death or love).

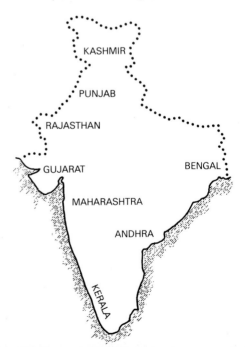

There is a huge variety of folk music in India. The different types of people vary not only in looks, language and customs, but also in their music. For example, the people from the snow-capped Himalayan region would sing different songs from the people who live in the hot sandy sea coast of the South. Here is a map showing some of the states of India. Each state has several types of folk music, but here is one example from each region. (To find out where the states are, look at the large map of India on page 47.)

Kashmir

The Kashmiris have an unusual type of folk music called the **Gulrez**, which means 'a folk tale'. The words are written by poets and sometimes the folk tale is as long as a thousand verses. Each verse is often sung to the tunes of popular songs.

Rajasthan

The women of the Rajasthan tribes do tricks while they are singing. They can perform difficult feats with swords, lamps, and sticks and still keep to the rhythm of their songs.

Kerala

The people of Kerala sing folk songs while they work. The pace of the music helps them to get through their work quickly. Each song describes the type of work that they are doing: farming, collecting the corn, grinding, fishing, etc. Fishermen hauling in their nets sing a rhythmic song as they pull.

Punjab

The most popular folk music here is called **Bhangra**. In this the women sing the tunes and the men dance to the music which is sometimes accompanied by drums, cymbals, and a stringed instrument.

▲ A folk musician from North India playing a two-stringed instrument

Andhra

In this southern state, there is a special kind of folk drama called **kuchipudi**. The actors dance, sing and act out plays in the open air, usually under the shade of trees or beneath a moonlit sky. The stories of the plays may be about an event in history or about life. The unusual thing about this folk drama is that there are no women in it and men play the female roles.

Bengal

The state of Bengal is well known for its poetry and music. The most popular kind of folk songs are sung by groups of wandering minstrels called **Bauls**. They earn their living from singing and playing music in the different villages. The themes of their songs are usually based on religion, life and nature. Their songs are often accompanied by a stringed instrument, a drum and a pair of cymbals. The music of the Bauls has attracted many western musicians including the famous Western folk singer Bob Dylan. Thousands of LPs of Baul music have been sold in Britain and the U.S.A.

Maharashtra

This is the only state in India which has war songs and dances. It is usually the men who dance to the accompaniment of a rhythmic instrument. The dancers have a stick in each hand which they strike while they are singing. The men are dressed like warriors and their sticks are meant to be swords.

Gujarat

The Gujaratis have a dance called **Garba**. In this, the men and women dance and sing, with sticks. Both the Punjabis and Gujaratis who live in England, still perform their folk music and dancing for festive occasions. Recently, many of these dances have been popularized in Indian films. You can see a photograph of Garba dancing on page 7.

13

◄ Two tribal musicians playing old trumpet-like instruments

Projects

1 Here is an example of a popular folk tune from Northern India. You can play it on any instrument or even sing it to 'la'.

Folk tune from Northern India

Questions

1 How did folk music begin in India?
2 What are the subjects that a folk song may be based on?
3 What is special about the folk drama called *kuchipudi*?
4 Who are the Bauls of Bengal?
5 Why is the folk music of Punjab and Gujarat becoming better known in India nowadays?

2 Think of any folk songs you know (from any country) intended to be sung while people work. List them, and say what kind of work people would be doing as they sang them.

Religious music

Most Indians follow their religion strictly. There are different places of worship to cater for the different religions. For example, *temples* are used by the Hindus, *churches* by the Christians, and *mosques* by the Muslims. Each religion has its own special kind of music.

In the Hindu temples the most common form of music is the **Bhajan**. In this the choir or congregation sings after a leader, accompanied sometimes by an orchestra. The music begins slowly but gets faster as it is repeated. Towards the end the Bhajan is sung very fast. The Bhajan may be based on ancient religious stories. It is interesting that one of the Beatles (George Harrison) recorded a song in the form of a Bhajan which reached the top of the hit parade in the early 1970s. It was called **Govindam**.

The Christians also sing Bhajans in their churches. The only difference is that the words are about Christianity. The priest sings the main part, followed by the congregation singing the response. In fact, the Christian Bhajan is very like the versicle and response found in Christian services all over the world. Christians in India also sing hymns as people do in churches everywhere.

Indian Muslims have a special form of religious music called **Qawali**, which is a combination of clapping, chanting, and singing. The music is meant to rouse the congregation to a religious trance. You can see a photo of a Qawali on page 33.

Muslims also have regular religious chanting in their mosques. You can hear a priest or **Imam** singing chants from the mosque every Friday, in most Muslim countries.

A Hindu religious singing group: lead singer and congregation ▶

Questions

1 Name the three main places of worship in India.
2 What is a Bhajan?
3 What kind of music would you expect to hear in a Christian church?
4 What kind of singing can you hear every Friday in muslim countries?
5 Name the Western pop song which was sung in the form of a Bhajan. Which famous pop star made it popular?

Projects

Here is one of the most popular Bhajans. It is sung at many Hindu religious gatherings even in the West. A western pop song was made out of the same tune and words in America and Britain, in the early 1970s. There are only two words '*Hari Krishna, Hari Rama*', which are the names of a Hindu God. The

Bhajan is repeated many times depending on the enthusiasm of the priest and the congregation. It is usual for the music to get faster as the tune is repeated.

Bhajan: 'Hari Krishna Hari Rama'

Ha-ri Krish-na ____ Ha-ri Krish-na ____
Ha-ri Ra-ma ____ Ra-ma Ra-ma ____

____ Krish-na Krish-na ____ Ha-ri ha-ri ____
____ Ra-ma Ra-ma ____ Ha-ri ha-ri ____

▼ The mosque in Regent's Park, London

Classical music

Indian classical music is quite separate from the music discussed so far. It is one of the oldest forms of music in the world and dates back nearly 2000 years. The classical music of Northern and Southern India is not the same. South Indian music is even older than the music from the North, and has developed in a different way.

North Indian music developed from ancient religious chants. These later became influenced by Arabic music in the 11th century (1000 years ago — when the Muslims invaded India). This was the beginning of North Indian classical music, as we know it today.

In the past, classical music flourished in the courts of the Indian princes who were called **Maharajas**. Musicians and other artists (such as dancers, actors, story tellers, sculptors, poets, and painters) were employed by the maharajas. They lived in the maharajas' palaces and music was rarely heard outside the courts, so there was little contact between court music and any other kinds of music. Classical Indian music remained pure and traditional for centuries because it was not influenced by other music. Each court had its family of musicians which specialized in a particular style of music. Each musical style was handed down by word of mouth from father to son through several generations.

A classical Indian painting of the god Krishna with musicians ▶ and *gopis* (milkmaids or shepherdesses). Paintings like this would hang in maharajas' palaces

East meets West

However, when the radio was introduced in the 1920s, classical music began to be heard outside the palaces of the princes. Since then, Indian music has been performed in many parts of the world. Indian classical musicians such as **Ravi Shankar**, Imrat Khan and Ali Akbar Khan play in all the large cities of the West. The famous sitar player Ravi Shankar visits England at least twice a year to play to a packed audience in the Royal Festival Hall.

Indian music has now become popular amongst Western composers and musicians. Composers such as Stockhausen, John Cage, Holst, Messiaen and Benjamin Britten have introduced Indian themes into their music. For example, Stockhausen wrote a work called *Mantra* which was inspired by Indian music. In the 1960s pop and jazz stars like the Beatles, Rolling Stones, Dave Brubeck, Larry Adler, Pink Floyd, Indo-Jazz Fusions, and Miles Davis used Indian musical ideas. For example, the Beatles used the sitar in their hit song *Norwegian Wood*. Even the Greek composer Theodorakis used sitars for his musical score in the film *Trojan Women.* One of the first Western musicians to play an important role in introducing Indian music to the West was the great violinist **Yehudi Menuhin**. There are L.Ps of him performing music with Indian musicians.

In a short space of time, Indian music has become part of the international music scene. Yet it has not changed much in its structure and is still played in the same way as it was centuries ago in the palaces of ancient India.

(Opposite) A tabla, or Indian pair of drums. The larger one is the bass drum, the smaller the treble. Notice the ring in the middle made from iron filings and rice powder. (See page 34)

George Harrison, one of the Beatles, with the Indian musician ▶
Ravi Shankar, who taught him the sitar

Questions

1 How old is Indian classical music?
2 How did Indian musicians earn their living in the past?
3 Where was classical music performed and how were musical styles passed on?
4 Name some Western musicians who have been influenced by Indian music.
5 What do you understand by the term 'classical music'? (Look it up in a music dictionary if you are not sure.)

Project

Listen to the L.P. *West meets East* which has Yehudi Menuhin introducing Indian music to the West. Then try and write down the various reasons why you think Indian music is different from Western classical music. (See *Books and records*, page 48.)

3 The form of Indian music

The four main elements

The music of Northern India is different from that of Southern India, although their origins are similar. Most of the music described in this book is North Indian, because most of the Indians who have settled in the West come from the Northern provinces.

At first Indian music might sound monotonous to a Western person (especially if he or she had never heard it before). This is not surprising, because anything that is new takes time and effort to understand. But in order to understand Indian music, you have to learn to accept a new way of listening and appreciating. The first step is to understand how it is worked out or structured. Once you know this, it will become easier to follow the music.

There are four main elements in Indian music — **drone**, **melody**, **rhythm** and **improvisation**. You therefore have to be able to recognize the various parts of Indian music by listening carefully, as Indian music is not written down. You can't follow it in a score, as you can a Beethoven symphony.

Drone

Before you begin to listen for rhythm and melody, you need to get familiar with the **drone**. This can be heard right through most performances. The drone can sound a little confusing to some people, because it is only two notes though played continuously. It takes time to separate the sound of the drone from the rest of the music. Once you get used to it, then you will be able to hear the rest of the music above the sound of the drone.

Melody

The next step is to listen for the main part, the **melody**. It is usually played by the main instrument such as the **sitar**, **sarod** or **flute**. The melody is based on a special selection of notes called a **raga**.

A drone instrument (tambura)

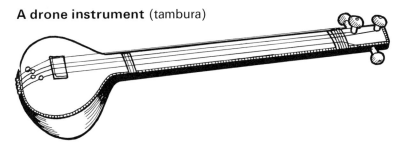

Three melody instruments (sitar, flute, sarangi)

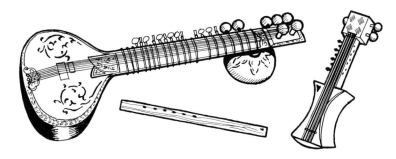

Two rhythm instruments (tabla, or pair of drums, and a folk double drum)

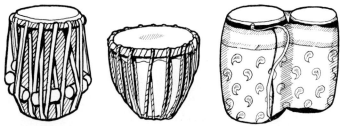

Rhythm

Next we have the rhythm, which is called **tala**. A tala is not just a time signature as used in Western music. It is a basic rhythm pattern or cycle with many complicated patterns within it. For example, think of this tune from *West Side Story*. The rhythm is repeated throughout the song.

1   2   3   1   2 3 1–2   1–2   1–2
I want to live in A mer - i - ca

A tala is repeated many times in a similar way, but with hundreds of complicated patterns within it.

As well as listening for the melody, drone and rhythm in Indian music, you have to know how it is all put together. This is done by **improvisation** and some composition. Since Indian music is not written down, musicians have to improvise (make up the music). But they have to improvise within a strict set of rules that fit into the raga and tala that they have chosen to play.

To sum it all up, an Indian performance begins with a drone, joined by the main instrument (perhaps the sitar) playing the melody. Later the music is accompanied by the rhythm which is played on the **tabla** (Indian drums). (Some performances are performed only with a drone and a main instrument, without a tabla accompaniment.) The music is slow to begin with, but gradually becomes faster and more complicated, ending in a great climax.

Questions

1   What are the four main elements in Indian music?
2   *a*   What is improvisation?
    b   What is a drone?
3   What kind of instrument plays the melody in Indian music?
4   Which instrument plays the rhythm?
5   How does the music begin and end?

Drones

The drone, as you already know, serves as a background for almost all Indian music. But Indian music is not the only music in the world which has a drone. Arabic, Turkish, Greek, medieval European, Celtic and Scottish bagpipe music has drones. Recently a pop song called *Amazing Grace* was played with a Scottish bagpipe and drone.

The Indian drone instrument is called the **tambura**. It has a long neck and four strings which are most often tuned to the **tonic** (the first note of the scale) and the **fifth** note of the scale. Sometimes the drone can be played to the notes of the tonic and the **fourth** note of the scale. The player usually places the tambura over his left shoulder with the gourd (the hollowed-out pumpkin base) resting on his lap. The notes are played in a steady rhythm, with the right-hand fingers strumming the strings continuously, one after another.

Three kinds of bagpipe

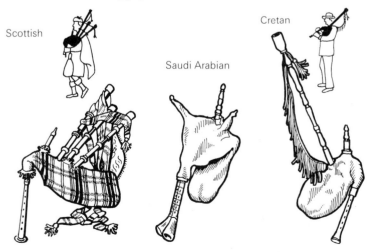

Scottish

Saudi Arabian

Cretan

Project

Playing a drone

The drone can be played on any instrument that can sustain each note and overlap the sounds. Obviously, it will be impossible to produce the exact sound of a tambura in the classroom. But instruments such as a steel drum, cello, piano, harmonium, melodica and recorder can be used. Divide into a few large groups or smaller groups playing different instruments. After playing each drone, exchange instruments with your ncighbour and play a different drone. Experiment with high and low notes and play together to create a 'sound piece'.

Drones

◀ A tambura being played

Ragas

The term **Raga** has a number of meanings. Some people translate it as a 'tune', others as a 'composition' and it has also been called an 'invocation' (calling of a God). The simplest way of understanding a raga is to call it a group of notes rather like a melody.

There are about 250 ragas in Indian music. Each one has its own particular mood and association. No one knows exactly why certain colours, pieces of music and sounds can make people happy, sad or excited. For example, if you went into a room that was painted bright red, how would you feel? Like colours, each raga has a special mood that can affect the listener.

Each raga is meant also to create a mental picture or image. The ancient Hindus believed that each sound had a specific colour and picture and it is thought that each raga was sung to call a particular God.

Different ragas are played at different times of the day. There are morning, afternoon, evening and night ragas. Some express happiness, courage or humour, while others express sorrow, peace or even anger. When a musician chooses his raga he thinks of all these things. This is why many musicians do not announce the raga that they are going to play until the actual time of the concert. In the past, musicians would only sing ragas at the time that they were meant to be sung. But nowadays the rules are not so strict and you can sometimes hear a morning raga being played in the evening.

A morning raga: the lady is hailing the rising sun with a fan in one hand ▶ and a napkin in the other. She is in a sorrowful mood

Different types of Raga

Lach'ha Bilaval is a 'happy' raga which is played in the daytime and it is very similar to the Western major scale. (Remember that a major scale generally expresses happiness while the minor scale expresses sadness.) Every raga has a special *ascending* (going up) and *descending* (going down) scale.

In a performance, the musician can only improvise on the ascending notes of the raga when he goes up and the descending notes when he comes down.

Lach'ha Bilaval

ascending	*descending*
C D E F G A B C	C B C B♭ A G F E D C

Malakosh

Here is an example of a night raga. It is called **Malakosh** and expresses peace and prayerfulness. In this raga the ascending and descending notes are exactly the same.

ascending	*descending*
B D E G A B	B A G E D B

Megha

Another raga which has a totally different mood to the one mentioned is **Megha**.

ascending	*descending*
C D F G B♭ C	C B C B♭ G F E F D C

Raga Megha is a seasonal one and is meant to be played during the monsoon rains. Megha means clouds. There is a story that when King Akbar's palace was burning, a girl sang this raga until rain came and put out the fire. A picture which illustrates this raga is the lord Krishna dancing with his wife Radha, who plays the drum, and a *gopi* (shepherdess), playing the cymbals. The background is of trees, flowers, and clouds.

Questions

1 What is a raga?
2 Why do musicians often leave it to the last minute to choose the raga they are going to play at a concert?
3 Give an example of a 'happy' raga.
4 What is the difference between a raga and a tune (in Western music)?
5 Name two ragas and explain their differences.

Projects

Playing a raga

1 Here is a selection of ragas. Each one has a mood and is usually played at different times of the day or night. But it does not really matter if your music lesson is in the day time and if the raga you are playing is a night one. Just before you perform each raga, think of its mood and then imagine the time of day that it represents. Divide into two large groups or small groups of two. Group 1 plays first, followed by Group 2.
Group 1 – xylophones or glockenspiels.
Group 2 – recorders or chime bars.
You can use any instruments that you like, but if you are in twos then each of you must have a different instrument.
Group 1 plays ascending scales.
Group 2 plays descending scales.
   You can exchange instruments and sometimes you can experiment with the sound by playing loudly and softly. Try to perform your parts from memory if you can.

1 Morning raga (Vibhas)

Mood – loveliness, sound of the early dawn.
(Drone notes C, A)

2 Afternoon raga (Bilaval)

Mood – pleasant and joyful
(Drone notes C, G)

3 Evening raga (Marwa)

Mood – restless and uncomfortable.
(Drone notes C, E)

4 Night raga (Malakosh)

Mood – peaceful and meditative.
(Drone notes B, E)

25

Raga with a drone

2 You have played some ragas in their ascending and descending patterns. Now it is time to play a raga with a drone. Use a suitable instrument for the drone and choose a melodic instrument for playing the notes of the raga. Divide the class into two groups. Group 1 plays the drone. Group 2 plays the raga melody.

   Remember always to begin the drone before the melody comes in. You can try and play a drone in the same way for the other ragas that you have played in 1 (the notes of the drone have been written on the side).

Marwa

You will notice that in this raga the drone notes are the first and sixth of the scale, instead of the usual first, fourth, or fifth. Some ragas have unusual drones like this one.

Talas

The word **Tala** comes from the syllable **ta** (representing the dance of the god Shiva) and **la** (the dance of his female companion).

Tala also means 'clap'. But now, it is usually thought of as a *rhythmic cycle*. In a Western composition, you will see a time signature (2 3 4) at the beginning of each piece. But despite the time signature, the pulse or basic rhythm of a Western piece can slow down or speed up as the composer wishes. (Listen to the *1812 Overture* or *Peter and the Wolf*.) In Indian music, however, there is one basic tala or rhythmic cycle which is played slowly at the beginning, and which gradually increases speed towards the end. Many complicated rhythms are added to the tala as decorative patterns.

It is generally accepted that there are 360 talas. But some are rarely played because they are either unpopular, or out of fashion, or too complicated. The first beat of the tala is the most important one. All rhythmic patterns and decorations have to begin and end on the first beat. In between, the tabla player can improvise his rhythms in any way he likes; but he must always finish improvising each time on the first beat of the tala. The tala's first beat is so important that it has a special name: **Sam**.

The most commonly played tala, called **Tintal**, has 16 beats. The strongest beats in this tala are the *1st, 5th* and *13th* beats.

X				X				O				X			
1	2	3	4	5	6	7	8	9	10	11	12	13	14	15	16

The **X** represents the **strong** beats (which are *clapped*) and the **O** means a **weak** or silent beat (which usually indicates a *wave* of the hand). When an Indian beats out a tala, he must *clap* on the strong beats and *wave* on the empty beats. The wave is very important because it helps to keep track of the rhythmic cycle.

▲ A harvest dance from Himachal Pradesh, North India

Indian audiences often clap to the tala or rhythm during a performance, and this is often the most exciting part of a concert. The tabla player can show off his skill and knowledge by playing very complicated and difficult rhythmic patterns, but he must always return in time to the Sam or first beat. Audiences enjoy following the tala and they clap enthusiastically when the tabla player comes back to the Sam.

Questions

1 What is a tala?
2 How many talas are there in Indian music?
3 How would you beat the silent and empty beats of a tala?
4 Why is the Sam (first beat) particularly important in Indian music?

Projects

Clapping a tala

1   Here are some talas that can be clapped. Divide into two large groups, or into twos. Group 1 counts out the beats of the tala in time. Group 2 claps out the main beats of the tala. You clap only on the crosses **X**. (Finger clicks can be used instead.)

On the silent beats marked **O** make sure that you give a gentle hand wave or make a silent gesture with the back of your hand.

Group 1 begins first by counting out the beats of the tala. Then Group 2 joins in, clapping out the main beats. Always end on the *first beat*. Try to clap each tala out from memory. You can use rhythmic instruments such as sticks and small cymbals on the claps.

Kherwa   *4 beats*
Group 1 begins counting 4 equal beats

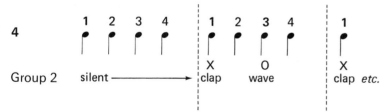

Dadra   *6 beats*
Group 1 count

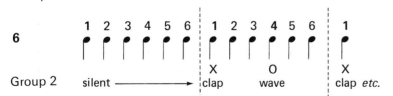

Rupak Taal   *7 beats*
Group 1 count

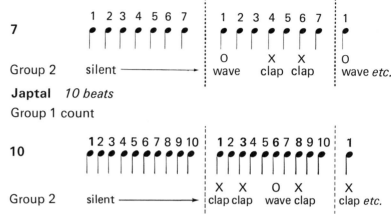

Japtal   *10 beats*
Group 1 count

Playing a tala

2   Now play a tala with percussion instruments. Avoid loud instruments such as the big drum or large cymbals. Sticks, wood blocks, castanets, bells, bongos and any kind of small drum can be used.

Divide into four groups. Group 1 counts out the tala with the claps. Groups 2, 3, and 4 play their parts on suitable instruments.

Kherwa   *4 beats*
Group 1 begins by counting and clapping out the tala.

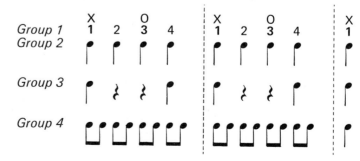

28

Improvisation on a raga

You have so far learnt that Indian music is based on the improvisation of a chosen raga and tala. You also know that there are special rules that have to be observed within each raga and tala. But now it is time to try and understand a little about the way in which musicians play a raga from beginning to end.

Each raga has four important notes. These four notes have to be emphasized at certain sections of the performance. They also have to be played in a certain way. The most important note, which is often repeated, is called the **Vadi** or King Note. The next important note is the **Samvadi** or Chief Minister, which follows the King Note everywhere. Then there is the **Anuvadi** or Servant Note. Lastly there is the **Vivadi** or Enemy Note which is not always used, because it produces discord or clashes with the sound of the raga.

The notes that are most prominent in a raga improvisation are the Vadi and Samvadi. The musician will focus his attention on these notes and treat them as the centre of improvisation.

An Indian performance usually begins with a slow introduction or **Alap** in which the soloist (or sitar player) introduces short tunes or phrases which emphasize the King Note or Vadi. There is no rhythmic beat in this section. The musician also gradually weaves out his melodies from the notes of the raga and brings out the Chief Minister Note and the Servant and Enemy Notes. He has to make sure that he emphasizes each important note, according to the mood of the raga.

For example, in a raga which has a peaceful mood the musician will make sure that the Enemy Note is not played too often, if at all. By skilfully emphasizing the main notes, a performer helps to create the mood of the chosen raga right from the beginning.

After the slow section, he adds a rhythmic pulse or beat to the music in the next section. In this section the soloist may be joined by the tabla player. Here the musician explores the mood of the raga even further. New melodic and rhythmic patterns are introduced and the music gradually gains speed.

This leads to the final section, when the music of both the tabla player and the main soloist gets faster and more complicated. Finally, there is a kind of **coda** where the musicians replay some of the music that has been played in the previous sections. The music gets even faster until it ends with a dramatic climax.

There are several other ways of playing a raga, but this is the most common one. Throughout the performance the musicians have to keep to the basic melody of the chosen raga and the rhythm of the chosen tala. Wrong selection of notes could spoil the mood of the whole performance.

▼ Some of the characters in a raga. Can you say who they are?

Questions

1 What are the four main notes of a raga?
2 Which are the notes that are emphasized in the introductory section?
3 How does an Indian improvisation usually end?

Projects

Playing a raga (melody) with a drone

1 Here is a simple tune made up from a raga. Divide into two groups. Group 1 plays the drone; Group 2 plays the melody or tune.

Make sure that the drone instruments can sustain each note. Each part needs to be worked out and practised before they are put together. It is important to remember that the drone should be played for at least four bars before the melody joins in. Begin by playing the music slowly and when you know how to play it well try to play a little faster each time (but always keeping in time with the beats).

2 Here is a very simple example of how this five-note raga is played in an improvisation at the beginning of a performance. The main note or Vadi is emphasized in the first bar. The Chief Minister or Samvadi is introduced in the second bar. The third and fourth bars have a short tune which has been made up from the five raga notes. V. and S. stand for Vadi and Samvadi.

You can play this piece on any melodic instrument.

Raga malakosh

(Opposite) An Indian musical group showing, left to right, ▶
sitar, sarod, tambura and tabla

4 The instruments
and their players

Indian concerts

During the time of the maharajas (princes of India) concerts were held in their luxurious palaces. The concerts were held in honour of special guests or just for the princes and their family. (The situation was the same in Europe before the 20th century when music was performed mainly for royal occasions in the homes of the aristocrats.)

Nowadays, music can be heard in various places. In temples people pray to God by chanting and listening to singers performing religious music. But music in the temples is not just an entertainment; it was, and still is, treated as part of the religious ceremonies. Concerts are also held in the open air. Folk musicians often perform under the shade of trees or underneath a moonlit sky. People usually sit on the ground or on wooden stools, and listen to the music. Concerts can also be heard in large concert halls all over India. In the time of the maharajas, concerts were free. But now people have to buy tickets.

In the West a typical concert has a conductor and orchestra playing the music of a composer, but in an Indian concert there are no conductors, orchestras or composers. You will only see a small group of two or three musicians accompanying the main performer. The music that is played has not been written down or composed. Instead, the performer creates or improvises his music around a main theme. A concert can last from three hours to all night in India. The length of the performance depends on the mood of the musician. Each piece of music usually lasts much longer than a classical Western composition such as a symphony or concerto. An Indian piece of improvisation usually lasts for about one hour. Before a performer begins to play, he may take up to half an hour to tune his instrument.

The performance will depend a lot upon the enthusiasm of the audience and the inspiration of the musician. Encouraging remarks from the audience help to inspire the musician's playing. In this way, an audience at a jazz concert is very similar to an Indian one. Both audiences show their approval and enthusiasm throughout the performance. In a typical Indian concert you will see the musicians sitting cross-legged on a carpet. There will usually be a pot burning sweet-smelling incense to create a pleasant aroma and peaceful atmosphere.

Questions

1 Name three places where concerts are performed in India.
2 What is the difference between a temple concert and an open air concert?
3 What are the main differences between an Indian concert and a Western one?
4 Why are Indian concerts longer than Western ones?
5 Why are jazz audiences similar to Indian audiences?

A Qawali, or Muslim religious concert. ▶
The lead singer is playing the harmonium. (See page 15)

The tabla and the tabla player

Most Indian classical performances are accompanied by a pair of drums called **tabla**. According to the ancient Hindu legends, Shiva (the god of music and dance) invented the drums. One story says that in the deep crevasses of the Himalayan glaciers, one often hears the 'thud' of heavy ice boulders falling down. These noises are believed to be from Shiva's drum.

The right-hand drum (or treble drum) of the tabla is called the **Daya**. The left-hand drum (or bass drum) is called the **Baya**. The tabla is played with the fingers and the palm of the hand, and the player sits cross-legged with both drums in front of him. The drums are made from a stretched outer layer of skin on the top, with a round black circle in the middle (made from a paste of iron filings and rice powder).

The tabla can play many more than two sounds. For example, on the treble drum (Daya) the tabla player can produce varied sounds by striking in different places with his fingers or with the palm of his hand.

There are special names or syllables for each of these rhythmic sounds. In the past, when music was not written down, tabla students learnt to play the drums through memorizing the names of each sound through a special 'drum language'. On the diagram opposite, each sound shows the area and way in which the drums should be played. (For example, **Na** is struck on the outer ring of the Daya by the tip of the index finger. **Tu** is the black circle struck by the cupped hand.)

A tabla player spends years learning to play the hundreds of talas and also memorizing the sound syllables. Together with this he has to study hundreds of complicated rhythms and play all of them well, either slowly or extremely fast. When you hear the tabla, towards the end of a performance, it is played so fast that it becomes impossible for the listener to keep track of the

▼ Indian drums: a tabla made of wood, a double drum and an unusual tabla made of clay

rhythms. Many Western drummers are amazed by the skills of Indian tabla players. Jazz drummers like Buddy Rich have studied Indian drumming and in fact a unique record was made in the 1960s by him and one of India's leading tabla players Alla Rakha.

The training of a tabla player, like a sitar player, requires great mental and physical discipline. The drummer Alla Rakha often mentions his years of training and practice of Yoga. He even used to hang from the ceiling to strengthen his arm muscles, so that his tabla playing would be even better.

Questions

1   What are the names of the two drums of the tabla?
2   How does the tabla player play the drums?
3   Which God invented the drums?
4   How did people learn to play the tabla in the past?
5   How is the sound **Na** played on the tabla?

Sounds played on surface of the tabla

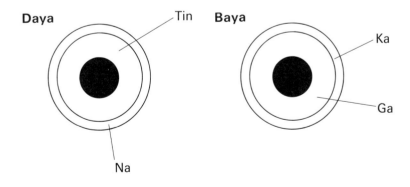

Na + Ga = Dha
Tin + Ga = Dhin

◀ A tabla player

35

Projects

Saying a tala

1 Divide into small groups of three (or three large groups). There are three parts: Group 1 counts, Group 2 claps, Group 3 pronounces the rhythmic sounds.

The sounds may be a little difficult to say as they are derived from an ancient Indian language called **Sanskrit**. They must be said with a rhythmic lilt.

Work out each part carefully. First put the counts and claps together, then put the sounds together with the claps and counts. Each person needs to concentrate on their part. You can exchange parts as you learn them. Remember that the counting begins first. We are going to use two talas that we mentioned before.

Dadra *6 beats* (count beats before clapping and saying the sounds)

Group 1 counts	1	2	3	4	5	6 →1
Group 2 claps	X			O		X
	Clap			Wave ———→		Clap
Group 3 says	Dhin	dhin	dha	dha	tin	na→Dhin

Kherwa *4 beats*
counted in 8 quarter beats

Group 1 counts	1	2	3	4	5	6	7	8 →1
Group 2 claps	X		X		O		X	X
	Clap		Clap		Wave		Clap →	Clap
Group 3 says	Dha	ge	na	tin	na	ka	dhin →	Dha

Playing a tala with a drone

2 Here is a simple version of the 16-beat **Tintal** tala, which you have already met. It is played in a 16 quaver beat cycle. The drone notes are C and G. Any rhythmic instruments can be used provided they are not too loud. Divide into two groups — rhythm and drone. Rhythmic instruments such as sticks, wood blocks, maracas, small cymbals and bongos will do well. Always remember to begin the drone four bars before you start. The bar lines are not really meant to be in a tala. They are used here for easier reading.

A third group could play the rhythm of the bottom line (the notes which have their stems down).

The sitar and the sitar player

The sitar is the most popular instrument of Northern India. It has existed in a similar form for nearly 700 years. It is a stringed instrument very similar to another much older stringed instrument from South India called the **Vina**. Both the sitar and the vina can be said to be from the same family — the lute family.

In Hindu legends the vina is always played by Saraswati, the Goddess of art, music and learning. It is believed that the God Shiva invented the vina because he was captivated by his wife's beauty. He made the vina according to her shape. The long neck of the instrument represents her body. The two supporting round gourds are her breasts and the metal frets are meant to be her bracelets.

▲ A painting of a young woman with a vina. She is followed by two gazelles, who are looking up at her, enchanted by her beauty

◀ A sitar player

37

▲ Another stringed instrument, the sarangi. Notice the sympathetic strings under the base of the main ones

There are six or seven main playing strings which are played with a wire plectrum. There are also 20 movable frets of curved brass which are adjusted to suit the various ragas and their notes. Under the base of the main strings are 19 unusual strings called **sympathetic strings**. These sympathetic strings vibrate when the main strings are sounded. They can also be plucked with the little finger of the right hand which often bleeds at the end of a long performance. The first string is very flexible and can be played in a unique way. Sitar players tend to use this string by pulling it gradually and sounding four or five notes in one pull.

The sitarist takes a long time to tune his instrument before he plays it. This is because Indian musicians are trained to listen for precise and exact tuning. Sometimes, in the middle of a performance, a sitarist may stop to tune up one of the strings.

To become a fully trained sitar player requires a vigorous training and fierce discipline from childhood. Some musicians have trained for over 20 years before they have allowed themselves to perform in public. Music students spend hours practising their instruments. They also need to have some knowledge and practice of meditation, yoga and the other arts. Teachers are treated with great respect and are called **Gurus**. It is traditional for students to greet their teachers or gurus by kissing or touching their feet.

Questions

1 How old is the sitar?
2 How was the vina invented?
3 How is the sitar played?
4 What are sympathetic strings?
5 What is the Indian name for a teacher?

Project

Playing a melody, tala and drone

Divide into three groups. Group 1 plays melody, Group 2 tala, and Group 3 drone. You must know by now what kind of instruments to choose for each group. The melody needs to be heard well above the drone and tala. Someone should clap out the tala right through.

The drone should be played for four bars before.

Other musical instruments

There are dozens of different Indian musical instruments. Some scholars think that India has the largest variety of stringed and percussion instruments in the world. Most of the ancient instruments are still used in their early forms and have remained basically the same thoughout the centuries.

The materials used in instrument-making are usually the ones found in the area where the instruments originated. Bamboo, gourds (hollowed out pumpkins), wood, clay, and skin are common materials.

The instruments played in classical Indian music are different from the ones used for accompanying folk music.

◀ An unusual Indian bell, hung from the mouth of a cobra

Classical instruments

The **Vina** is one of the oldest stringed instruments. Its ancestor is the ancient Egyptian lute which existed some 4,000 years ago. The long neck is made from wood and there are two round gourds (hollowed out of pumpkins) at either end. There are 28 movable frets and seven wire strings which in early times could have been made from animal gut or strong grass. The four melody strings are played with a wire plectrum or a glass egg which slides up and down the string. The player usually sits cross-legged with one of the gourds resting on his left knee. The vina is a popular household instrument in South India (as the piano is in England). It is often played by women.

▲ Modern vina player. Notice the gourd resonator resting on her knee

▲ Fifth century terracotta relief of a goddess with a lute-type instrument

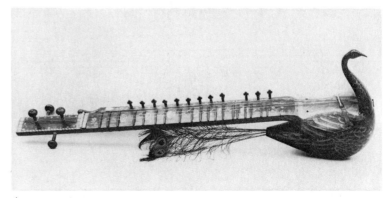

▲ A mayuri, ancestor of the sitar, in the form of a peacock

The **Shehnai** is a North Indian wind instrument and originally came from Persia. It is similar to an oboe with a double reed, but it has no keys on the staff. Instead there are 7–9 holes which are played as on a recorder. In a shehnai concert the drone is always played by other shehnais. It is a popular instrument in temples and weddings, and is used also in folk music.

▼ Two shehnai players and a drummer

▲ A sarod player

The **Sarod** is a stringed instrument that is smaller than a sitar. It is made from one large piece of wood and has a metal strip along the neck. This gives it an unusual sound. It has 25 strings, of which 10 are plucked with a coconut plectrum. The other 15 are sympathetic strings which resonate when the main strings are played. There are no frets and the left hand moves along the metal fingerboard with a vibrato (as it does on the violin).

41

Folk instruments

The **Ektara** is a very simple instrument. It has one string and is made out of a hollow gourd or clay bowl, covered on one side with animal skin. It is commonly used by villagers to accompany their folk songs.

The **Dholak** is a drum used mainly by travelling musicians. It is 50 cm long and made out of one piece of wood, which is hollow right through. Both ends are covered by skin. It is played mainly by hand and is used particularly for village weddings.

▼ Musicians playing an ektara (below) and a dholak (right)

Questions

1 What materials are used to make instruments?
2 What is a gourd?
3 Name two classical instruments and two folk instruments.

Project

Draw and label as many Indian instruments as you can. Choose three and describe them in your own words.

(Opposite) Elephant relief from a temple in Belur, South India ▶

From gods and goddesses to the present day

Music can be traced back to the ancient legends of the Gods and Goddesses. According to the old Hindu scriptures, the Lord of the Universe came out of the sea in the form of a fish and handed four books on religion and music to human beings. These books, called the **Vedas**, are believed to have been written over 3,000 years ago.

The original authors and patrons of music were supposed to be the Gods and Goddesses. The first performer of dance and music was the God Shiva. He is said to have sung with such power that he could enchant his audience. The Goddess Saraswati is always represented as the Goddess of art, music and learning. She is usually pictured as seated on a white lotus with a vina in one hand.

Each God and Goddess is associated with a musical instrument or aspect of music. It is said that the ten-headed demon God Ravana invented an instrument in this way: he was carrying a mountain and found it unbearable, so he decided to sing in order to ease his pain. But he needed an instrument to accompany him. So he chopped off one of his heads, cut out a nerve from his body and created the **Ektara** or one-stringed instrument.

Apart from the stories, there are also several books on musical theory. The oldest book on Indian music was written during the third century. It contains detailed accounts of musical scales, intonation, melodic patterns and musical topics. The earliest type of music performed was religious chants, which later developed into scales and ragas.

The first North Indian musician known was Jayadeva, who lived at the end of the 12th century. He was born in Bengal, and he wrote a book of songs called the *Gita Govinda*. Since then, many authors have written about the musical theories of their time. The 14th and 15th centuries were the most important in the development of music. The Moghul emperors and Indian princes did a great deal to extend music. The emperor Akbar who lived in the 16th century encouraged musicians to develop their art.

During the last few centuries, India has made great advances in the study of music, and there are schools of music all over the country. In fact, there are universities and colleges in various parts of the world (for example, the University of California at Berkeley) where you can study Indian music.

Bronze statuette of ▶
the god Shiva, dancing

44

Some stories and legends

The ancient books have recorded many stories about how music has had power over people, lulled restless children to sleep and even calmed down mad elephants. In one story, we are told about a young girl who is mourning over the dead body of her brother. All of a sudden an elephant appears and tries to drag away the corpse. But the girl in her fear sings a melodious raga which makes the elephant forget what he is doing. Instead he stands enchanted by the music.

There is another story about the emperor Akbar and his court musician Naik Gopal. There is a tradition that whoever sings Raga Dipaka (Song of the earthen lamp) will be destroyed by fire. It is said that this emperor ordered his musician to sing this powerful raga. The musician tried his best to be excused from singing it, but the emperor insisted. So before he began singing, the musician placed himself up to his neck in the water of the river Jumna. But as soon as he began singing, the waters began to boil around him and he was in agony. He begged his emperor to allow him to come out of the water, but the emperor refused, because he wanted to see the power that music has over human beings. The story ends by saying that the musician burst into flames in the water and his body was turned into ashes.

◀ Painting of the Raga Dipaka. A prince, riding on an elephant, holds the earthen lamp while his servant fans him. The elephant has a lamp in his trunk, also

45

◀ Painting of the god Krishna, seated on a cushion of lotus flowers spread on a serpent. He is playing the flute.

Another interesting story tells about another musician from emperor Akbar's court, called Tan Sen. It is said that when Tan Sen died, his son sang a sad raga beside the corpse of his father. During the performance, the dead musician's body lifted up its hand and blessed his son. There is a belief in India that if you eat the leaves of the tree near Tan Sen's tomb, then you will inherit a beautiful voice.

Questions

1 According to the ancient legends, how did human beings learn about music?
2 Who is the Goddess Saraswati?
3 How was the Ektara invented?
4 What was the earliest kind of Indian music?
5 Which people helped to develop music during the 14th and 15th centuries?
6 What do the ancient books say about the power of music?
7 Why did the emperor Akbar make Naik Gopal sing Raga Dipaka?
8 What happened to Naik Gopal when he sang Raga Dipaka?
9 Who was Tan Sen?
10 What happened when Tan Sen's son sang over his father's body?

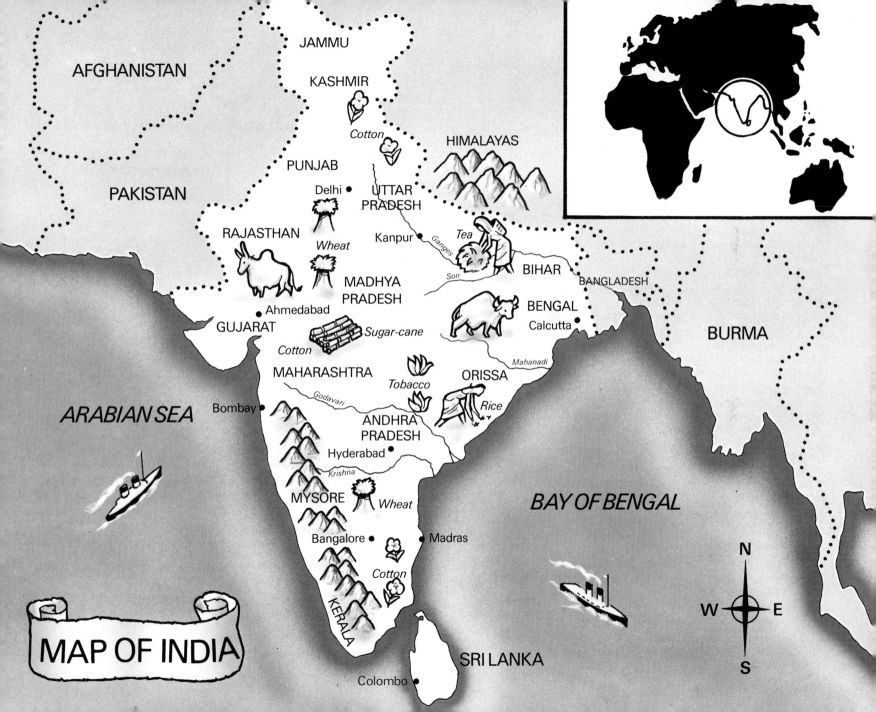

MAP OF INDIA

Books and records

The following books and aids will provide teachers with some starting points for introducing Indian music to their classes.

P. Holroyde *Indian Music* Allen and Unwin 1972

R. and J. Massey *The Music of India* Kahn and Averill 1977

Pratapaditya Pal *The Classical Tradition in Rajput Painting* The Pierpont Morgan Library and The Gallery Association of New York State 1978, distributed by Oxford University Press
(a reasonably priced catalogue of 78 Indian classical paintings, in black and white, with descriptive notes)

Neil Sorrell and Ram Narayan *Indian Music in Performance* Manchester University Press 1980
(a book and cassette package which offers a practical guide to the structure of Indian music)

G. Vulliamy and E. Lee *Pop, Rock and Ethnic Music in School* Cambridge University Press 1981
(includes a chapter on Indian music)

The Horniman Museum *Musical Instruments* I.L.E.A.
(includes pictures and descriptions of Indian instruments; single copies available from the Horniman Museum, multiple copies from the Inner London Education Authority at County Hall, London SE1)

The following records are a selection from a large number available from the EMI catalogue. Two record shops in Southall, London (ABC Magazines (01-574 1319) and India Record House (01-574 4739) hold large stocks of Indian records.

Yehudi Menuhin, Ravi Shankar *West meets East* (3 volumes): ASD 2294, EASD 1346 and ASD 3357

Ravi Shankar *Two Raga Moods* EASD 1325

Ustad Ali Akbar Khan *Morning and Evening Ragas* (*Music of India* series) ALPC 2
(features the sarod. Spoken introduction by Yehudi Menuhin)

The *Music of India* series (several volumes) features well-known Indian musicians playing a variety of instruments.

Western pop records influenced by Indian music

The Beatles *Sergeant Pepper's Lonely Hearts' Club Band* PCS 7027
(the song 'Within you, without you' has a tabla accompaniment, sarangi and a drone)

Terry Riley *Rainbow in curved air* CBS 64564
(uses repeated phrases on keyboard instruments based on the Indian tala system)

John McLaughlin *Shakti* CBS 81388
(combines guitar with Indian violin)

Useful addresses

The Commonwealth Institute
Kensington High Street, London W8 (01-602 3246)
(arranges visits to schools by Indian musicians and dancers)

Government of India Tourist Office
21 New Bond Street, London W1 (01-493 0769)
(supplies brochures and information about India for pupils' project work)

The Gramophone Company of India Limited, U.K. Branch
Unit 8, Boeing Way, International Trading Estate
Southall, Middlesex UB2 5LB (01-843 0650/0670)
(Distributor for EMI of their records of Indian music. Supplies catalogues and further information)

Sussex Publications Ltd.
FREEPOST, Poulshot, Devizes, Wiltshire SN10 1BR
(produce a series of cassette/slide sets, videotapes and films called *Music and Society*. The series features dance, religion and social habits, music and arts and crafts, all related to the everyday life of people in the Middle East, India and China.)